Grade 1

SCALES (one octave)

Fingers only / *tirando* or *apoyando*

G major

F major

Thumb only / *tirando*

A minor harmonic*

E minor harmonic*

* the natural minor form may be offered instead of the harmonic form:
for examples, see www.abrsm.org/naturalminorexamples

ARPEGGIOS (one octave)

Tirando

G major

E minor

Grade 2

SCALES (one octave)

Fingers only / *tirando* or *apoyando*

* the natural minor form may be offered instead of the melodic/harmonic form specified above:
for examples, see www.abrsm.org/naturalminorexamples

Thumb only / *tirando*

CHROMATIC SCALE (one octave)

Thumb only / *tirando*

Guitar
Scales & Arpeggios
ABRSM Grades 1–5

Why practise scales?

Welcome to this book of technical requirements for guitar. Practising scales, arpeggios and other patterns plays an essential part in developing a guitarist's skills. Time devoted to these exercises within each practice session will improve many aspects of technique, such as hand positions, co-ordination and left-hand shifts. In addition, the sense of key and pattern acquired through familiarity with scales and arpeggios has several benefits: it speeds up the learning of new pieces, helps develop evenness of line, quality of tone and good legato playing, builds aural awareness, and increases familiarity with the geography of the fingerboard.

For the exam

Tempo

The candidate should aim for a tempo that achieves a clean, uniform tone and a rhythmic flow without undue accentuation. Recommended minimum speeds are printed in this book for each requirement.

Tirando/apoyando

In Grades 1–4, candidates may choose to play 'fingers-only' scales either *tirando* (free stroke) or *apoyando* (rest stroke). From Grade 5, these scales must be prepared with *both* right-hand techniques. The *tirando* stroke is expected for all other requirements.

Choice of fingering

The fingerings given in this book, while not compulsory, are strongly recommended. However, the examiner will not comment on the choice of fingering unless it interferes with the performance. Any combination of alternating right-hand fingers may be used for the 'fingers-only' scales; those involving the ring finger are no longer compulsory.

On the day

The examiner will usually ask for at least one of each type of requirement set for the grade. These must be played from memory.

The examiner will be looking for:
- confident, controlled and consistent tone across the pitch range
- an even and positive sense of rhythm
- accurate, fluent and, above all, legato realization of the different scales, arpeggios and other patterns.

Notes on the requirements & practical points

Types of scale: fingers-only, thumb-only, combined

Conventional scales played by alternating right-hand fingers feature in all eight grades, but in Grades 1–2 they are complemented by lower-octave scales to be played with the thumb only. It is recommended that while the thumb plays these one-octave scales the right-hand fingers are planted on the upper strings, thus helping develop the independence of thumb movement so vital for good polyphonic playing.

In Grades 3–5, 'thumb-only' scales are replaced by two-octave 'combined' scales in which the lower octave is to be played by the thumb and the upper octave by alternating fingers. These scales encourage a stable right-hand position and consistency of tone when changing between thumb and fingers. This is greatly facilitated by planting the index finger on its string from the very beginning of the scale so that it is ready to continue into the upper octave. At the change-over point the thumb should in turn be planted, ready to resume from the same note on descending.

Interval scales

Scales in sixths, tenths, octaves and thirds are introduced progressively from Grade 3, to be played together as well as broken. The ability to play in this range of intervals is fundamental to a harmonic understanding of guitar music and a thorough working knowledge of the fingerboard. It also greatly assists the development of left-hand positioning and finger independence, as well as enhancing the overall co-ordination of the hands. Playing interval scales broken can be approached in the same way as playing them together, i.e. with right-hand thumb and finger planted simultaneously with every crotchet beat.

Arpeggios and broken chords

All arpeggios from Grade 3 (including dominant and diminished sevenths) are to be played with no over-ringing of adjacent notes. This is easily achieved by following the given left-hand fingerings, which exclude half-barrés and open strings. The non-over-ringing prescription does not apply to arpeggios at Grades 1 and 2.

By contrast, broken chords are to be played with notes over-ringing – a natural consequence of each triad covering three separate strings. It is not necessary for the candidate to damp notes that ring beyond the triad.

Distinguishing between over-ringing and non-over-ringing in this way is invaluable in helping the student understand the function of different musical elements, e.g. whether a specific arpeggiated passage is part of a melodic line or an accompanying harmonic texture.

Left-hand fingering

- The left-hand fingering suggested in this book reflects the progressive use of the fingerboard on a grade-by-grade basis. Position signs (in Roman numerals) are the primary source of information; these are complemented by occasional left-hand finger numbers and string numbers. No position signs are given at Grade 1 as everything is to be played in the 1st position.

- In the Grade 1 fingers-only scales, the 4th finger is recommended for 3rd-fret notes, so that the left hand can more easily remain in alignment. This also helps prepare the hand for interval scales and polyphonic music. Some candidates, however, may find lower-string 3rd-fret notes easier with the 3rd finger, so Grade 1 thumb scales give 3rd *or* 4th finger for these.

- With hand-size again in mind, the 4th finger is not called upon to play at fret 5 on the D string until Grade 2. Similarly, it is only at Grade 3 that it is indicated for fret 5 on the A string, and Grade 4 the bottom E string.

Right-hand fingering

- For all types of scale, right-hand fingering is given only for the first example in each grade.

- The pattern ♩ ♫ ♬ has been chosen so that the rhythmic emphasis shifts between alternating right-hand fingers, such that if, for example, the first pair of quavers is played *im*, then the first pair in the subsequent bar will be played *mi*. This pattern promotes the development of right-hand rhythmic control and flexibility.

- The recommended right-hand fingerings for arpeggios (as well as dominant and diminished sevenths) have been chosen to work in tandem with the given left-hand fingerings and are largely determined by the occurrence and frequency of string crossings. They are designed to encourage a stable right-hand position and to explore a variety of thumb and finger combinations that reflect as closely as possible how passages such as these might be played in actual pieces.

Reference must always be made to the syllabus for the year in which the exam is to be taken, in case any changes have been made to the requirements.

Contents

ARPEGGIOS (one octave)

Tirando

C major

D major

A minor

D minor

Grade 3

SCALES (two octaves)

Fingers only / *tirando* or *apoyando*

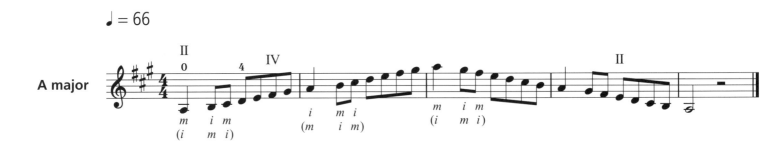

A major

B minor harmonic

Thumb and fingers combined (thumb for lower octave, fingers for upper octave) / *tirando*

G major

E minor melodic

AB 3413

CHROMATIC SCALE (one octave)

Fingers only / *tirando* or *apoyando*

INTERVAL SCALE (one octave)

Together *and* broken / *tirando*

BROKEN CHORD (one octave)

With over-ringing / *tirando*

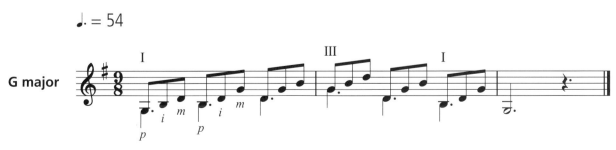

ARPEGGIOS (two octaves)

Without over-ringing / *tirando*

♩. = 44

G major
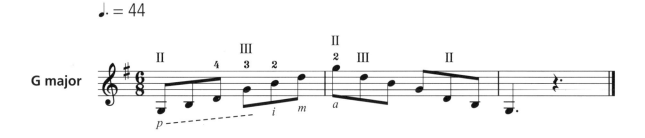

A major
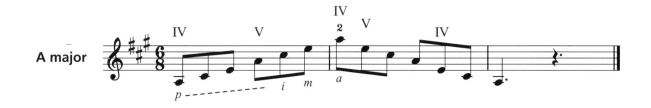

E minor
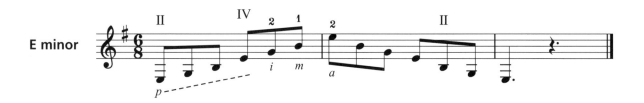

B minor
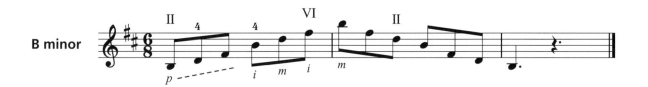

AB 3413

Grade 4

SCALES (two octaves)

Fingers only / *tirando* or *apoyando*

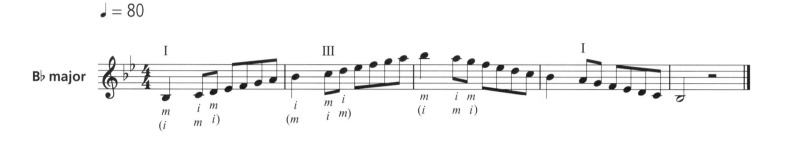

Bb major

B minor melodic

Thumb and fingers combined (thumb for lower octave, fingers for upper octave) / *tirando*

F major

F# minor harmonic

CHROMATIC SCALE (two octaves)

Thumb and fingers combined (thumb for lower octave, fingers for upper octave) / *tirando*

INTERVAL SCALES (one octave)

Together *and* broken / *tirando*

G major in tenths

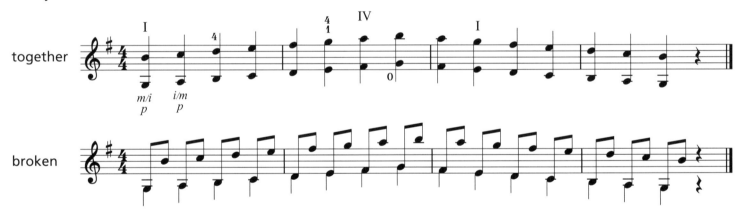

A minor harmonic in sixths

BROKEN CHORD (one octave)

With over-ringing / *tirando*

C major

ARPEGGIOS (two octaves)

Without over-ringing / *tirando*

F major

B♭ major

B minor

F♯ minor

DOMINANT SEVENTH (one octave)

Without over-ringing / *tirando*

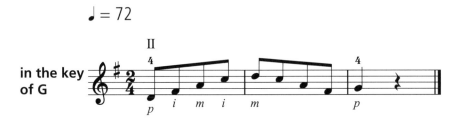

AB 3413

Grade 5

SCALES (two octaves)

Fingers only / *tirando* and *apoyando*

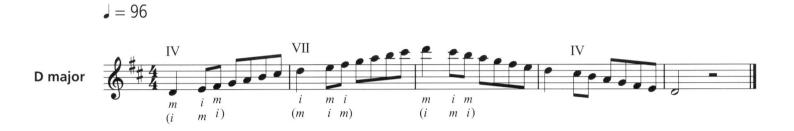

Thumb and fingers combined (thumb for lower octave, fingers for upper octave) / *tirando*

CHROMATIC SCALE (two octaves)

Thumb and fingers combined (thumb for lower octave, fingers for upper octave) / *tirando*

INTERVAL SCALES (one octave)

Together *and* broken / *tirando*

A major in sixths

F major in octaves

A minor melodic in tenths

together

broken

BROKEN CHORD (one octave)

With over-ringing / *tirando*

♩. = 66

E minor

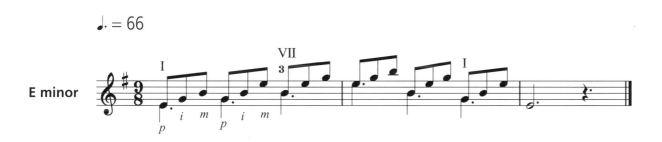

ARPEGGIOS (two octaves)

Without over-ringing / *tirando*

♩. = 56

D major

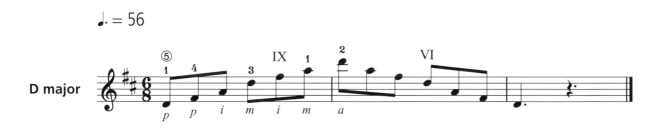

E major

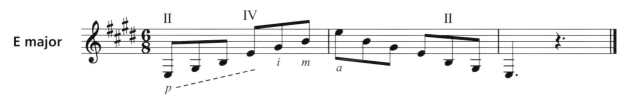

A minor

G minor

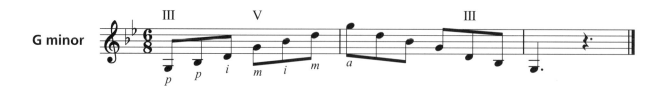

DOMINANT SEVENTH (two octaves)

Without over-ringing / *tirando*

♩ = 84

in the key of D

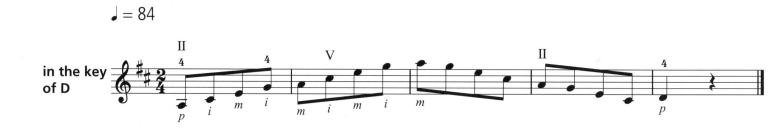

DIMINISHED SEVENTH (two octaves)

Without over-ringing / *tirando*

♩ = 84

starting on A

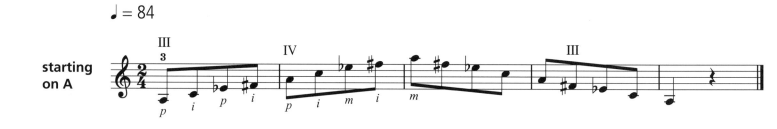

Printed in England by Caligraving Ltd, Thetford, Norfolk